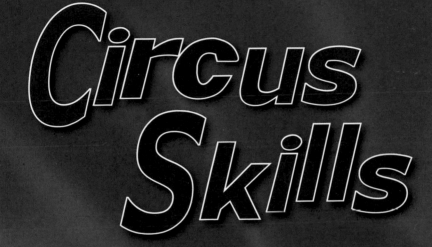

Circus Skills

by Cathy West

StarStruck

Circus Skills

by Cathy West

Illustrated by Elly Walton

Published by Ransom Publishing Ltd.
Radley House, 8 St. Cross Road, Winchester, Hants. SO23 9HX
www.ransom.co.uk

ISBN   978 184167 479 7

First published in 2011

Illustrations copyright © 2011 Elly Walton
Photographic images copyright ©: cover – Steve Rabin; pages 4, 5 – Who-is-me; pages 6, 7 – H. Powers, U.S. Library of Congress, Miroslava Arnaudova; pages 8, 9 – Susanna Fieramosca Naranjo, Evgeniya Moroz; pages 10, 11 – Magisphoto, Debs, Alexander Yakovlev, Helder Almeida; pages 12, 13 – Who-is-me, Chris Johnson, Jared Alden, U.S. Library of Congress; pages 14, 15 – Barry Sherbeck, Kevin Tavares; pages 16, 17 – Andreas Fink, David Shankbone, Rhett Sutphin; black satin, passim – Jon Helgason.

A CIP catalogue record of this book is available from the British Library.

The rights of Anita Loughrey and of Stephen Rickard to be identified as the authors and of Elly Walton to be identified as the illustrator of this Work have been asserted by them in accordance with sections 77 and 78 of the Copyright, Design and Patents Act 1988.

Circus Skills

3

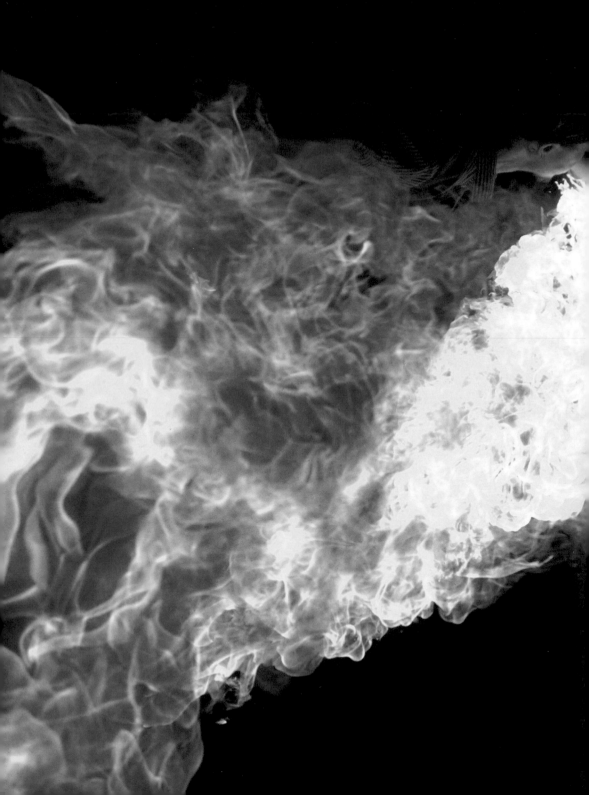

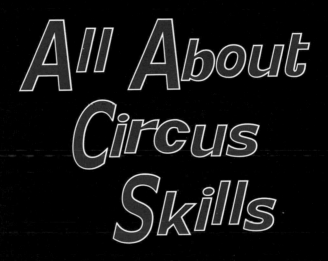

All About Circus Skills

The circus has been popular
for hundreds of years.

In the old days a circus had

   a big tent (called the big top)

   jugglers

   acrobats

   clowns and

   performing animals.

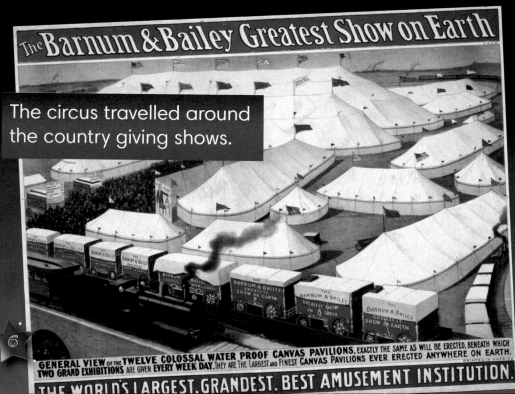

The circus travelled around
the country giving shows.

The Barnum & Bailey Greatest Show on Earth

GENERAL VIEW OF THE TWELVE COLOSSAL WATER PROOF CANVAS PAVILIONS. EXACTLY THE SAME AS WILL BE ERECTED, BENEATH WHICH TWO GRAND EXHIBITIONS ARE GIVEN EVERY WEEK DAY. THEY ARE THE LARGEST AND FINEST CANVAS PAVILIONS EVER ERECTED ANYWHERE ON EARTH.

THE WORLD'S LARGEST, GRANDEST, BEST AMUSEMENT INSTITUTION.

But things changed.
People stopped having
animals in circuses.

They thought it was cruel.

Circuses became
less popular.

But now circus skills are
more popular than ever!

Popular circus skills

Trick cycling

A unicycle is a bicycle with one wheel.

You need good balance!

Juggling

Some performers juggle with balls.

Others use clubs, beanbags, fire torches or even knives.

Clowns

Some people are afraid of clowns.

You need
great balance.

Tightrope

A tightrope is tight.

If it's not tight, it's
called a slack line.
This is a slack line.

Dangerous circus skills

Some circus skills are very dangerous.

I don't need to say this but ...

DON'T TRY THIS AT HOME!

Fire eating

This is even harder than it looks.

Sword swallowing

It takes about ten years to learn how to do this.

Trapeze

It's only dangerous if you let go!

Tightrope

You can walk on it, sit on it, and even cycle across it.

Just don't fall off.

Remember!

DON'T TRY THIS AT HOME!

11

Amazing skills!

In 1859 Charles Blondin crossed the Niagara Falls on a tightrope.

Then he did it again – wearing a blindfold.

And again. This time, he carried a man on his back.

Once he stopped half-way across to cook his breakfast!

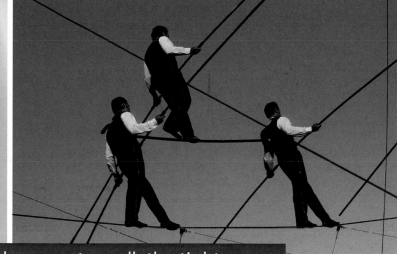

Seventeen years later, Maria Spelterini crossed the Niagara gorge on a tightrope.

She did it wearing peach baskets strapped to her feet!

Here's another way to walk the tightrope. The person on top gets a free ride!

Where can you see circus skills?

There are many different circus skills.

You can see these skills in lots of places:

 At the carnival or fair.

 In the park.

 In the streets, when you go shopping. (It's called street theatre.)

 At parties.

 Even at the beach.

And, of course, at the circus.

Most circus skills don't need lots of equipment.

Just a few props:

 juggling balls

 stilts

 hoops

 a good outfit.

Learning circus skills

Do you want to learn some circus skills?

You can learn some kinds of circus skills on your own.

It just needs lots of practice.

You could try these skills on your own:

Riding a unicycle

Juggling

Acrobatics

16

Stilt-walking

Some circus skills are more difficult. Some are dangerous.

For these skills, you need a good teacher.

Fire dancing

Sword swallowing

Walking the tightrope

Remember!

Many schools and clubs run **workshops** on circus skills.

Look in your local newspaper - or on the **Internet**.

DON'T TRY THESE AT HOME!

Chapter One

Juggling

The local circus was holding auditions. Yasmin and Sam waited with the others. Soon it would be their turn.

'My sister's in charge of the circus,' Sam said.

'Why do you need to audition, then?' asked Yasmin.

'My sister only takes the best people.'

'I've been practising my juggling for weeks,' Yasmin said. 'I hope I'm good enough.'

'Let's have a go.' Sam pointed at the juggling balls Yasmin was holding.

Yasmin passed them to him. He flipped them in the air, spun them behind his back and balanced one on his nose.

Yasmin clapped.

'You're brilliant,' she said. 'Are you going to do juggling for your audition too?'

'No. I want my act to be more thrilling,' Sam grinned. 'I've got plans for something extra special.'

Chapter Two

Extra special

It was Yasmin's turn. She went into the audition room.

She started to juggle the balls. One of them landed on her head.

'No! No! No!' Poppy the circus owner cried. 'You're not good enough! Next!'

Yasmin picked up the juggling balls. She opened the door to leave. Next, it was Sam's turn.

But Sam was nowhere to be seen.

Then Poppy's mobile phone rang. It was Sam.

'Where are you, Sam?' Poppy asked. 'Look out of the window? Why?'

Poppy rushed to the window. Yasmin followed her.

They could see Sam. He was at the window of the building opposite. A wire joined the two buildings.

Sam climbed out of the window on to the ledge.

'Cool! He's going to do a high-wire act,' Yasmin said.

Chapter Three

Dare devil

Sam did not move. He stood with his back pressed against the wall. His eyes were shut tight.

'Help! I can't move!' Sam yelled.

'He must be scared of heights,' said Poppy.

'I'll save you!' called Yasmin. She scrambled out of the window. Then she walked carefully across the high-wire towards Sam.

Yasmin had perfect balance. She reached the other side easily. She helped Sam off the window ledge, back into the building.

'He's safe,' Yasmin shouted across to Poppy.

'You both get back here NOW!' Poppy yelled.

Chapter Four

Face the music

Sam and Yasmin rushed across the street back to the audition room. Poppy was waiting. Her face was red. Her hands were clenched. She glared at them.

'I have never seen anything so ... .' Poppy paused.

Poppy turned to Yasmin, 'So ... brilliant! You're a natural. I want you in our circus, to do the high-wire act.'

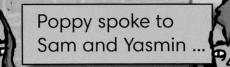

Poppy spoke to Sam and Yasmin ...

I have never seen anything so ...

... so brilliant!

Yasmin, you're in the show.

You're my new high-wire act!

'As for you ...' Poppy frowned at her brother.

'Sorry!' Sam whispered.

'I thought you were going to do juggling. You're an ace juggler,' Poppy said.

Sam smiled. 'I can even juggle with fire.'

'And I can juggle on the high-wire!' added Yasmin.

Yasmin threw the juggling balls in the air. She dropped all three of them.

'Noooo!' said Poppy and Sam together.

Curtain Call

acrobat

acrobatics

auditions

balance

big top

carnival

Charles Blondin

clown

equipment

fire torch

fire eating

flying trapeze

high-wire

hoops

juggler

juggling

juggling balls

Maria Spelterini

performing animals

practice

props

slack line

stilts

street theatre

sword swallower

tightrope

trapeze

trick cycling

unicycle

workshops